ALOHA ALBATROSS

For my own little Egg.
- FD

For my dance partner, Alex, and our River Willow.
- KC-W

A STUDIO PRESS BOOK

First published in the UK in 2023 by Studio Press,
an imprint of Bonnier Books UK,
4th Floor, Victoria House, Bloomsbury Square, London WC1B 4DA
Owned by Bonnier Books,
Sveavägen 56, Stockholm, Sweden

www.bonnierbooks.co.uk

1 3 5 7 9 10 8 6 4 2

Written by Francesca Dryden
Designed by Maddox Philpot
Production by Emma Kidd

A CIP catalogue record for this book is available from the British Library
Printed and bound in China

ALOHA ALBATROSS

Francesca Dryden

illustrated by

Kimberlie Clinthorne-Wong

STUDIO
PRESS

On the island of O'ahu, the Gathering Place, live thousands of Laysan albatrosses.

This is a story
about three very
special birds.

Palila loves to feel the wind on her wings as she soars high over the ocean.

Anuenue loves
to dance.

She clicks
her beak

and bobs her head as the waves of the Pacific Ocean crash on the shore.

Palila has been flying over the ocean for many weeks and feels her home calling to her.

Anuenue dances by herself.
She wishes she had someone
to dance with, like the other
albatross couples.

As the sun sets over O'ahu,
Palila lands. Her wings are weary
from her time at sea.

She wants to rest and sleep, but
she notices a bird dancing on
the shore, alone.

Anuenue dances
for the ocean.

She clicks her beak
at the white foam
and bobs her head
for the waves.

Palila watches her beautiful dance,
wanting to join in but not knowing how.

With a click of her beak, Palila tells Anuenue how graceful her dancing is.

Anuenue bobs her head,
showing Palila how to feel
the ocean's song.

Anuenue and Palila dance
together as the stars and
moon light up the sky.

They dance together for many moons, learning the other's rhythms.

Anuenue knows that she will soon lay
an egg, and the only bird she wants
beside her is Palila.

Together, the birds build a nest
beneath an ironwood tree.
Palila can see the ocean from
their new home.

Anuenue takes to the wing, searching for food.

When she returns she sits on their egg, keeping it warm beneath her feathers.

Palila flies across
the ocean.

She fills her
beak and belly
with fish.

One bright morning, Palila
returns to Anuenue. Together
they watch as a tiny crack
appears on their egg.

Soon more cracks appear on the egg
and a fluffy, grey head emerges.

Palila and Anuenue look at their chick in wonder. They bob their heads in a dance of love.

Ano looks at his mothers, and bobs his tiny head as best he can, eager to join in.

Laysan Albatrosses live the longest, out of all the birds in the world and the oldest albatross, Wisdom, recently turned 70. She is still raising chicks every year on Midway Atoll, the island where she was born in the middle of the Pacific Ocean. However, the small islands and atolls that albatrosses nest on are rapidly washing away into the ocean due to the rising sea level, and some birds are finding new places to raise their chicks. The story you have just read is based on real events. Just an hour from the busy beaches of Waikiki in Honolulu, Hawaii sits a nature reserve called Kaena Point. At Kaena Point, several hundred Laysan Albatrosses come back to lay their eggs and hatch their chicks each year. Laysan Albatrosses began nesting there in the 1990s after their breeding island in the Northwestern Hawaiian Islands disappeared into the sea. However, when the albatrosses began arriving, researchers noticed that there were more females than males. Since albatross parents fly huge distances across the ocean to find food for their chicks, they need two parents to raise a chick. But unlike other animal species, albatross chicks can have two mums or a mum and a dad! About a third of female albatrosses have chosen to pair with other females to raise their chick since they cannot find a male partner. Their egg is still fertilised by a male, but they raise it with their female partner. Similarly to all other types of albatross pairs, the two female albatrosses take turns caring for their chick. They also take turns laying eggs. Most albatrosses mate for life and will stay with their mate until death.

Lindsay Young, Ph.D.
Wildlife Biologist
Pacific Rim Conservation